Published by TROIKA

First published 2018

Troika Books Ltd
Well House, Green Lane, Ardleigh CO7 7PD
www.troikabooks.com

ISBN 978-1-909991-81-1

1 2 3 4 5 6 7 8 9 10

Printed in Poland

A ZETTER & WHITE PRODUCTION

INVASION OF THE SUPERVILLAINS

RAPS AND RHYMES TO WORRY THE GALAXY

FEATURING....

AND MANY MORE...

CRIMINAL CONTENTS

PASTA MAN

PASTA MAN DATA FILE

Secret ID – Peter Paster
Top power – Evades enemies by morphing into a spicy hot curry
Place or planet of origin – Luigi's Restaurant, Milan
Deadliest enemy – Chinese Noodle Lady
Other stuff – Lives in fear of being frozen, dried or canned

Pasta Man

He's wiggly and wriggly
And comes from sunny Italy
Though don't be tricked by his Latino charms
For this deceitful Pasta Man
Has formed a cunning master plan
That's guaranteed to cause us great alarm

He really isn't tons of fun
Throws meatball bombs at everyone
Squirts poisonous tomato sauce as well
Spaghetti arms he has a few
To tie you up and trap you too
Accompanied by horrid garlic smells

He wasn't born but fried and boiled
In water, herbs and olive oil
Till rotten luck revised his recipe
A tragic kitchen accident
Created this unpleasant gent
When smothered in some radioactive cheese

So if he is approaching you
You know exactly what to do
Just run away as swiftly as you can
Linguine or lasagne
There's a big chance they will harm ya
If they're served up by that nasty Pasta Man

The CHEWING GUM Kid

THE CHEWING GUM KID DATA FILE

Secret ID – *Polly Pink*
Top power – *Can stick anything and anyone with her chewing gum*
Place or planet of origin – *Sweetden*
Deadliest enemy – *Chewing Gum Removal Machine Man*
Other stuff – *Currently developing a deadly bubblegummy gun*

The Chewing Gum Kid

Your hands are glued
Your feet are glued
Your legs and arms
She'll glue them too
You can't run away
Yet you wish you did
Nobody escapes the Chewing Gum Kid

Just twelve years old
She'll freeze you cold
You're permanently
Placed on hold
No trickier type
In the candy shop
The Chewing Gum Kid can never be stopped

Though sugar-skinned
Her flavour's sour
Her gummy gun
Gives her great power
With chasing police
Sticking to the street
The Chewing Gum Kid is so hard to beat

Your hair is glued
Your teeth are glued
Your ears and nose
She'll glue them too
But there are worse criminals
You could meet
'Cause the Chewing Gum Kid...
Only steals your sweets!

HARDCORE

HARDCORE DATA FILE

Secret ID – Rocky Stone

Top power – Karate chops bricks in half with his nose

Place or planet of origin – Building site, Southwark, London

Deadliest enemy – Kid Bulldozer

Other stuff – No set of scales is robust enough to take his weight

Hardcore

Hardcore
Born on a building site
Hardcore
Gargles with dynamite
Hardcore
Everyone's enemy
Hardcore
Anti-celebrity

Hardcore
Such a destructive guy
Hardcore
Lifts hippopotami
Hardcore
Covered in bandages
Hardcore
Eats concrete sandwiches

Hardcore
Stronger than chilli sauce
Hardcore
Don't ask him out of course
Hardcore
Wears metal underwear
Hardcore
(Still owns a teddy bear)

Hardcore
Running a hundred miles
Hardcore
Teeth like a crocodile's
Hardcore
Headbutting aeroplanes
Hardcore
Tell me his name again
Hardcore
Tell me his name again
Hardcore

Mwahahahahaha!
(Or How to Become a Supervillain)

To defeat superheroes
Is a difficult thing
You could use nasty weapons
Plot and plan deadly schemes
You may mix poison potions
Build a laser-powered car
But you must emit an evil laugh
Mwahahahaha!

You might wear flashy costumes
Build a robotic brain
Hold a planet to ransom
Have a spine-chilling name
Forge a lasting alliance
With a warlord from Mars
But you must express an evil laugh
Mwahahahaha!

You can strengthen your muscles
Gain the power of flight
Or become an immortal
So you never will die
Maybe form your own army
And destroy a distant star
But you must unleash an evil laugh
Mwahahahaha!

It's important, essential
It's a tool of the trade
As without it you'll struggle
Score the lowest of grades
You should practise then practise
Practise, practise really hard
Until you possess an evil laugh
Mwahahahaha!

PROFESSOR MADD'S MUTANT LIVES!

PROFESSOR MADD'S MUTANT DATA FILE

Secret ID – I was too scared to ask him
Top power – Turns people to jelly
Place or planet of origin – The Madd Lab
Deadliest enemy – The Ultimate Superhero
Other stuff – Even uglier than his passport photo

Professor Madd's Mutant Lives!

With a thousand nuts
And a thousand bolts
Metal, plastic, glass
Plus a zillion volts
A creation's born
At the crack of dawn
Professor Madd's Mutant lives!

Standing ten feet tall
Hear him grunt and growl
At the lightning flash
And the wild wind's howl
Are those shrieks and shouts?
Then there is no doubt
Professor Madd's Mutant lives!

Big magnetic boots
Tatty shredded clothes
Check his massive head
And his razor nose
Jagged rotten teeth
Such a lab-born freak
Professor Madd's Mutant lives!

Skin of grimy grey
Add a hint of mauve
Watch his stomping feet
Cracking up the road
Banging at your door?
Then you'll know for sure
Professor Madd's Mutant lives!

If he's rising from his slab you
Better run or else he'll grab you
Professor Madd's Mutant lives!

BOOM!

DIAMONDIA DATA FILE

Secret ID – Ida Mond
Top power – All-round toughness
Place or planet of origin – The Selenic Galaxy
Deadliest enemy – The Invisible Lady
Other stuff – Diamonds are worthless on her planet as they are so plentiful

DIAMONDIA

Diamondia

Although she's very beautiful
Polite and so presentable
Will dazzle and delight you too
It doesn't mean she's good

Shiny shimmer of her skin
Hides the frozen soul within

Her body's indestructible
Her wealthiness immeasurable
Her value is incalculable
But what price is your life?

Fingers fire diamond darts
As she slowly steals your heart

Her surface is unscratchable
She's crafty and uncatchable
Her meanness is unmatchable
The superheroes say

If you see her up in space
Never gaze upon her face

Her dress and style are glamorous
Her reputation infamous
Diabolical and dangerous
Most deadly through and through

Hardest substance known to man
Keep your distance if you can

Although she's very beautiful
Polite and so presentable
Will dazzle and delight you too
It doesn't mean she's good

BAD

WRONG

VILE

MEAN

N4

EVIL

make
war
not peace

VILLAINOUS SNIPPET
Although superheroes aim to do at least one good deed each day, supervillains attempt to cancel them out with at least one bad one.

It's Good to Be Bad

It's good to be bad
So it's bad to be good
Since I was a child that's what I've understood
Them heroes are boring
Us villains are cool
Don't you get a kick out of breaking the rules?

It's nice to be mean
So it's mean to be nice
You want to enjoy life then take my advice
All laws can be broken
All orders transgressed
The way of the baddie is brilliant and best

It's kind to be vile
So it's vile to be kind
This mayhem I'm making's my way to unwind
To conquer the Universe
Who would want more?
It's dull to have peace but it's fun to have war

It's right to be wrong
So it's wrong to be right
Some say black is black although I say it's white
I'm threatening chaos
In your neighbourhood
It's good to be bad so it's bad to be good

Knucklehead

I'm Knucklehead
That's who I am
Thicker than a strawberry jam
Cleverness is not for me
I can't add up one plus three
All my power's in my fists
When I punch I never miss

I'm Knucklehead
I'm strong but dim
Muscles fat yet mind is thin
Tough as steel I feel no pain
Mega body, weedy brain
Always fail when stealing things
Cash and cars and diamond rings

I'm Knucklehead
Who no-one fears
Nothing much between my ears
Though the mightiest you've met
I don't know my alphabet
I've got weapons that don't work
Often nicknamed "Super Jerk"

I'm Knucklehead
I go to gyms
Pick a sport I'm bound to win
Still I'm hopeless planning crimes
Bruised and beaten every time
Superheroes say I'm daft
So if you meet me please...don't laugh!

KNUCKLEHEAD DATA FILE

Secret ID – Dan Dunce
Top power – Punches quite hard
Place or planet of origin – Dozyville
Deadliest enemy – His mirror's reflection
Other stuff – Frequently spells his name
   omitting the silent "K"

MADAM BEE

MADAM BEE DATA FILE
Secret ID – Beatrice Black
Top power – Supersonic stings
Place or planet of origin – Insectoid
Deadliest enemy – Anyone with strong insect spray
Other stuff – Gets extremely cross if mistaken for Ms Wasp or Miss Hornet

Madam Bee

Madam Bee, Madam Bee
Zipping round your head
Buzzing sound
All around
Like a very long zed
Not somebody you'd want
As an arch enemy
Madam Bee, Madam Bee
Madam Bee, Bee, Bee

Madam Bee, Madam Bee
Stripes of yellow and black
Poison sting
On the wing
Swooping down to attack
With her menacing swarm
Flying wild and free
Madam Bee, Madam Bee
Madam Bee, Bee, Bee

Madam Bee, Madam Bee
Honey powers her might
Watch her race
Into space
Like a meteorite
In the hive
She'll survive
While her rivals all flee
Madam Bee, Madam Bee
Madam Bee, Bee, Bee

Madam Bee, Madam Bee
Madam Bee, Bee, Bee

VILLAINOUS SNIPPET

Superhero School rules are virtually
the opposite of these.

Welcome to Supervillain School

Welcome to Supervillain School
To be a good baddie you will follow our rules

1 Run down corridors, don't walk
2 When teachers are speaking, always talk
3 Respect the banning of school uniform
4 Strive hard to be bottom of your form
5 Letting off stink bombs will be rewarded
6 Truanting's excellent and won't be recorded
7 Be discourteous, impolite and rude
8 When in the dinner hall throw your food
9 It's cool wearing tattoos and jewellery
10 *(Apart from this book)* avoid reading and the library
11 Bring ray guns and laser cannons into class
12 If sitting exams avoid gaining a pass
13 Practise each day being dastardly and evil
14 Never, ever offer to help needy people
15 Combing your hair is a definite no-no
16 Washing your hands is a total no-go
17 Those doing homework will be expelled
18 Ignore morning break and lunchtime bells
19 Remember, rules are important that's why we make them
20 All students must now promise to break them!

I. B. Bad

Mr I B Bad
Headteacher
Supervillain School

23

Stink Bomb

Who's got an aroma
That will put you in a coma
Cause your hair to part as well?
It's a supervillain
As repulsive as he's chilling
Flattens you with just his smell

Stink Bomb's what they call him
'Cause his stench is so appalling
Twice as strong as any skunk's
No bouquet of flowers
Can suppress his pongy powers
Hold your breath or you'll be sunk

Such an evildoer
Born and bred inside a sewer
Niffier than grandad's socks
Gives off an emission
That is bound to have you wishing
You could have your nostrils locked

Owns a secret hideout
(I'm suggesting that you keep out)
In a massive rubbish bin
Costume best forgotten
Tatty mouldy, green and rotten
Dripping mud and oil and gin

Watch out – he might smear you
Always keep some perfume near you
And a clothes peg on your nose
If you touch together
You would need to bathe forever
Stink Bomb's whiff will not let go

STINK BOMB DATA FILE

Secret ID – Mr B O'Fumes
Top power – Stinkiness
Place or planet of origin – Hong Pong
Deadliest enemy – Princess Perfume
Other stuff – His smell is so
powerful it can blow open a safe

RED ROSE

RED ROSE DATA FILE

Secret ID – Rosie Redd
Top power – Scratch skills
Place or planet of origin – Kew Gardens
Deadliest enemy – The Green Fly
Other stuff – Hangs out with wanted
supervillains Lily White and
Yellow Daffodil

Red Rose

Claws of toxic thorns
That will cut you every time
Once a pretty flower
Now she lives a life of crime

Piercing blood-red eyes
Sure to pin you to the wall
Power is her goal
No compassion shown at all

Burning acid smile
Flowing hair of emerald green
Though the heroes try
They will never take this queen

Hides herself away
In her Garden of Lost Souls
Tackle her with care
Or she'll fill you full of holes

Puffs of perfumed gas
Shooting from her petal gloves
Soaring through the sky
Like a missile high above

Uniform of silk
Double "R" upon her vest
Do you think you'll win
If you put her to the test?

Claws of toxic thorns
That will cut you every time
Once a pretty flower
Now she lives a life of crime

Dear Supervillains,

I'm writing to say I was so shocked to find
When I opened your new book to read the inside
I saw many facts about your dreadful deeds
Your thirsting for power, revenge and for greed
Your big-headed boasting about acting tough
Your arrogant bragging about fighting rough

It's definitely not for the eyes of our children
Best kept out of reach and most carefully hidden
Away in the attic and far from their sight
Preventing some terrible nightmares each night

You should be including some pleasant things too
E.g. superheroes, the great work they do
Rescuing cities, defeating space creatures
You may gain support then from parents and teachers

I'm sorry I cannot come to your defence
But you're such a dangerous influence
And as for you two, Chris White and Neal Zetter
I think that the both of you should know far better
Positive role models? There are none here
Just vicious vile villains for youngsters to fear

Ok my rant's over, this is where I stop
I'm sending your scary book back to the shop!

Yours,

Mr P Parker

Dear Supervillains,

Have you ever considered a truce with Miss Meteorite?
I'm pretty sure she wouldn't use her heat powers if

The Supervillains' Reply

Dear Mr P Parker

Shops tell us this book's been snapped up from their shelves

So we'll let our sales figures speak for themselves

Heroes are boring but villains exciting

Chill out Mr Parker - and thank you for writing

DOCTOR DYNAMITE DATA FILE

Secret ID – Stevie Strong
Top power – Strength of body AND character
Place or planet of origin – Jim's Gym
Deadliest enemy – Beach Bully
Other stuff – Is he villain or hero?
   The arguments continue...

Revenge of the
Seven Stone Weakling

While wearing trunks upon the beach
I tried hard to impress
As everybody laughed at me
I skulked off to get dressed

But four guys kicked sand in my face
Girls looked the other way
And though the sun shone high above
My world was grim and grey

My muscles were mere tiny bumps
My skin was white and pale
I vowed I would improve myself
Become a model male

I signed up at my local gym
My aim to toughen up
On entering a marathon
I gained a winner's cup

My arms and legs were tree trunks
And my six-pack stood so proud
"The time's arrived for sweet revenge!"
I shouted out aloud

I shopped at Costume Central
Bought my supervillain clothes
Then hunted down those bullies
And bashed each one on the nose

Now they're all frightened of me
Shrink and shrivel at my sight
From seven stone weakling to 90 kilo strongman
I'm **Doctor Dynamite**

THE RHYME THIEF

time
looking... we took same

THE RHYME THIEF DATA FILE

Secret ID – Wilma Wordsmith
Top power – Stealth
Place or planet of origin – Lexicon 7
Deadliest enemy – Any poet or rapper able to
  rhyme quicker than she can steal
Other stuff – It's rumoured the Rhyme Thief is
  collecting every rhyme she has stolen so she
  can publish her own book of rhyming poetry

The Rhyme Thief

Watch out for the Rhyme Thief
She is bound to steal your rhyme
If you try and make one
She will take it every …

Beware this wicked woman
Who is ruining this poem
Where's she likely next to strike?
We have no way of …

She sees it as a challenge
And she sees it as a game
Collecting all the words we're using
When they sound the …

You'll know when she has visited
You'll find an empty space
Once there was a rhyme
But there's a gap now in its …

Your verses, raps and odes
Should all be hidden from her sight
Mind your back she might attack
As you sit down to …

Stop this ghastly supervillain
Burglar and crook
Replace the rhymes she's stolen
And don't let her spoil this …

The Right Name

(For any supervillain, selecting the right name is extremely important)

Got my powers, got my costume
In my quest for infamy
Got my master plan and gadgets
Now my name – what could it be?

All the best ones have been taken
There aren't many left to pick
I will know it when I hear it
It will be a perfect fit

It must strike a note of panic
Causing people such a scare
As their legs turn into jelly
And they lose most of their hair

Don't want "Shadow", "Anti", "Mega"
Don't want "Dark" or "Doom" or "Death"
I've decided to be different
Then you'll know me from the rest

Don't want "Night" or "Ice" or "Fire"
Names of animals won't do
Nor will birds or fish or insects
Those ideas are overused

"Zapping Zetter", "Power Poet"
Are not titles that appeal
But I like alliteration
So please call me..."Nasty Neal"

MISTER GREY

MISTER GREY DATA FILE

Secret ID - I am too bored to say
Top power - I am too fed up to tell
Place or planet of origin - Nowhere very interesting
Deadliest enemy - Nobody worth mentioning
Other stuff - When teaming up with Ms Psychobabble
    (see next poem) both quadruple their powers
    (Now where's my wallet?...)

Mister Grey

Mister Grey they say, will bore you half to death
You'll be under his spell in a single breath
A most unusual superpower
Astounding and unique
When he decides to rob you
All he has to do is speak
Then he'll make off with your money
As you slowly fall asleep

Mister Grey they say, has had this skill since he was born
One word in your direction
You'll immediately yawn

He's as dull as his surname
As dull as racing snails
As dull as drying paint
As dull as biting nails

Mister Grey they say, will deactivate your brain
He's tedious, tiresome, monotonous, mundane
No imagination, no conversation
Like a train stuck forever
In the same railway station

He's as dull as maths homework
As dull as grating cheese
As dull as washing up
As dull as counting peas

But his boredom is his weapon
So don't let him come too near
If he tries to talk to you
Poke cotton wool into your ears
Or he'll hypnotise you, mesmerise you
Then mess with your head
Till you find yourself penniless
Lying snoozing in your bedzzzzzzzzzzzzzzzzzzzzzz

MS PSYCHOBABBLE

MS PSYCHOBABBLE DATA FILE

Secret ID – Suki Bobble

Top power – Mind control

Place or planet of origin – The Arctic (on Neptune, not Earth)

Deadliest enemy – Magnetic Me

Other stuff – Once accidentally hypnotised herself and remained in a trance for three whole weeks

Ms Psychobabble

Weaving words
Round your head
You'll repeat
What she said

Planting thoughts
In your brain
Sentences
Causing pain

Hear her chant
All the time
Echoing
Through your mind

Hypnotised
You'll do wrong
When enslaved
By her song

You're a page
In her book
You're the bait
On her hook

Hide your eyes
If she's near
As she talks
Close your ears

Weaving words
Round your head
You'll repeat
What she said
You'll repeat
What she said
You'll repeat
What she said

BOOM!

MATTER

ANTI MATTER

DANGEROUS EXPERIMENTS FOR SUPER VILLAINS

PROFESSOR MADD

black holes

HUGE MISTAKE!

massive mess

VILLAINOUS SNIPPET

All three people who bought Professor Madd's infamous book, "Dangerous Experiments for Supervillains", accidentally blew themselves up when trying to mix matter with antimatter.

Matter & Antimatter

(A poem warning children NEVER to attempt this most
dangerous experiment devised by Professor Madd)

Mixing matter with antimatter
It isn't very bright
The Galaxy will be destroyed
The Sun will lose its light
Don't play with scientific stuff
That you don't understand
If you mix matter with antimatter
Things will get out of hand

Mixing matter with antimatter
Is dangerous and rash
The cosmos will disintegrate
In one almighty flash
It's something Albert Einstein said
While working in his lab
If you mix matter with antimatter
It's bound to turn out bad

Mixing matter with antimatter
Would be a huge mistake
A big black hole would swallow us
Just like you'd eat a cake
As Stephen Hawking warned us all
When talking to the press
If you mix matter with antimatter
You'll make a massive mess

Mixing matter with antimatter
Is reckless and unwise
You'll cause a cataclysm
In which everybody fries
I've seen it in the movies
And it's not good news my friend
If you mix matter with antimatter
Our Universe will end...
BOOM!

MISS METEORITE

MISS METEORITE DATA FILE

Secret ID – Lena Star

Top power – Withstands extreme temperatures
(which has helped her to fly closer to
the Sun than any other known being)

Place or planet of origin – Magma 6

Deadliest enemy – Water Fool

Other stuff – Speaks 127 non-Earth languages

(The supervillains have kindly agreed
a short truce with one superhero and
allowed her to have a poem in their book)

Miss Meteorite

Wooooooooooooooooooooooooooooooooooosh!

Deep in the night
A laser light?
A satellite?
A bird in flight?
A soaring kite?

A stunning sight
At such a height
Watch it ignite
And burn so bright
With heat pure white

All power and might
Strong, lean and slight
(No cellulite!)
Hot dynamite

When in a fight
Don't get uptight
Who'll help your plight
And put things right?

To our delight
That shining knight
Miss Meteorite!
Miss Meteorite!
Miss Meteorite!

Zoooooooooooooooooooooooooooooooooom!

FATHER TIME DATA FILE

Secret ID – John Smith

Top power – Ability to age anyone and everything

Place or planet of origin – Everywhere

Deadliest enemy – Super Senior

Other stuff – His wife is the lesser-known Mother Time

Father Time

I'll steal your years away from you
And snatch your precious days
You'll feel them drifting from your grasp
While still trapped in my gaze
My mystic, magic hourglass
Controls each grain of sand
As you grow fragile, frail and grey
With one wave of my hand

Tick-tock, tick-tock, tick-tock
I can cause your clock to stop

Those heroes muscular and strong
Don't stand a chance with me
Alive and young at 21
I'll turn them 63
The sharpened silver scythe I wield
Will cut you in the end
So everyone's my enemy
And nobody's my friend

Tick-tock, tick-tock, tick-tock
I can cause your clock to stop

Now who'll prevent my darkest deeds
Controlling life itself?
I'll lay more age upon you
Or will slowly drain your health
Though hidden in the shadows
I am never far behind
Try as you might to stand and fight
You'll not beat Father Time

Tick-tock, tick-tock, tick-tock
I can cause your clock to...

robodroid

ROBODROID DATA FILE

Secret ID – Do robotic droids really have secret identities?

Top power – A zillion gigabyte computer brain

Place or planet of origin – Silicon Valley, California

Deadliest enemy – Thunderstorm

Other stuff – Beats all supervillains and superheroes at chess

RoboDroid Has Rusted

RoboDroid slept out in the rain
He's broken down and rusted
His disintegrator ray worked yesterday
Yet now it's bent and busted

You'd better fetch an oilcan fast
Crime capers could be in his past
Will this adventure be the last?
RoboDroid has rusted

RoboDroid's gone kinda stiff
His jaw's too tight for talking
The grating sound you hear around's
The noise he makes when walking

He's starting to squeak
He's starting to creak
From supervillain to super freak
RoboDroid has rusted

He's corroded, oxidised
He doesn't look too clever
A shower neutralised his power
Defeated by bad weather

He's bright orange (though was green and red)
If only he'd worn a plastic costume instead
The newspaper headline that I saw said
"RoboDroid has rusted"

No longer invincible, he's rooted to the spot
No longer indestructible, he now decays and rots
His armour instructions state "avoid water"
But he forgot
RoboDroid has rusted

Yes RoboDroid's like an old tin can
While his deadly enemies plot and plan
He's turned the colour of a fake suntan
RoboDroid has rusted

WD 40

FZZZZZTTT!

OOOOF!

SQUEEEAK!

SIGH!

VILLAINOUS SNIPPET

There are no Data Files on sidekicks as the supervillains who helped produce this book didn't think they were important enough to have them.

07

Only a Sidekick

I'm only a sidekick, fed up, frustrated
Underpaid, undervalued, underrated
I never trained at Supervillain School
So feel inadequate, feel uncool
Soon you won't remember me at all
I'm only a sidekick

It's tough at the top, but rougher at the bottom
Constantly defeated, forever forgotten
A minor character, a virtual unknown
No high-tech jet, fast car or phone
No colourful costume, or supervillain name
If injured in action, they'll find another the same
Today I was arrested, and jailed yet again
I'm only a sidekick

I always have to defuse that bomb you see
Fight powerful heroes much stronger than me
Though a baddie I'm not your main enemy
Just a foot soldier
With limited prospects of growing older
I'm only a sidekick

You want a loud explosion, you only get a pop
You want a glass of water, you only get a drop
You want a juicy orange, you only get a pip
You want a massive dinner, you only get a chip
You want a four-leaf clover, you only get a three
You want a supervillain, you only get me
I'm only a sidekick

PAINTBALL

PAINTBALL DATA FILE

Secret ID – Violet Van Gogh

Top power – Deadly accurate so hits targets from 2km

Place or planet of origin – LotsaPotsaPaint Ltd
   (paint factory), Hull

Deadliest enemy – Paintbuster

Other stuff – Shoots rotten eggs instead
   when out of paintballs

Paintball

Paintball
A truly terrible teen
The most colourful villain you've ever seen
A rainbow explosion
On the attack
Red, orange, yellow
Green, blue
SPLAT!

Paintball
Creates a collage of crime
Dressed in glittering pink and luminous lime
Sneaking in shadows
Paint gun attached
Red, orange, yellow
Green, blue
SPLAT!

Paintball
Beware her spectrum of sin
Doing exactly what it says on her tin
Acrylic or oil
Gloss, silk or matt
Red, orange, yellow
Green, blue
SPLAT!

Paintball
Playing a dangerous game
She'll stop you, rob you then graffiti her name
A poisonous palette
So watch your back
Red, orange, yellow
Green, blue

SPLAT!
SPLAT!
SPLAT!
SPLAT!
SPLAT!

AAARRGGGHH!!!

VILLAINOUS SNIPPET

Red wine, red paint, red ink, ketchup and green Venusian blood (dyed red) have all been used in place of human blood in movies.

I Hate the Sight of Blood

I want to be a villain
I would be if I could
But something holds me back a bit
I hate the sight of blood

It makes me sick and squeamish
I shrivel at the stuff
Though ketchup's fine on which to dine
I just say "no" to blood

A most unpleasant liquid
Types O or A or B
Blood may be cool in vampire school
But blood's uncool to me

If we were locked in battle
And wrestling in mud
I wouldn't let you lose red juice
I cannot cope with blood

While fighting superheroes
I'd aim to only bruise
Forego that haemoglobin 'cause
Blood's not the path I'd choose

All villains now reject me
Don't want me in their club
Suggesting I find other jobs
I hate the sight of blood

SUPERVILLAIN
CLUB
MEMBERSHIP
DENIED

53

TURBONAUT

TURBONAUT DATA FILE

Secret ID – Reggie Rocket

Top power – Speeeeeeeeeeeed

Place or planet of origin – Brands Hatch

Deadliest enemy – Sister Speed

Other stuff – Once he broke the sound barrier so badly
scientists took three weeks to stick it back together

Turbonaut

The horizon is humming
Feel the atmosphere thrumming
There's a criminal coming
Such a devilish sort
He's Turbonaut

Every window is shaking
Solid buildings are breaking
Populations are quaking
Villainy is his sport
He's Turbonaut

Through the city he's belting
Like a hurricane pelting
Watch his training shoes melting
He can outrun a thought
He's Turbonaut

Silver costume of leather
Holds his body together
Burns the Sun in hot weather
Very rarely outfought
He's Turbonaut

With his heart and pulse throbbing
There's a bank he is robbing
Call a hero to stop him!
But can he ever be caught?
He's Turbonaut

VILLAINOUS SNIPPET

Of the 3,646,765 threats of revenge made by supervillains only two have ever been carried out successfully.

Next Time...

You think that we're beaten
You think that we're broken
We're sorry to bring you bad news
Wipe smiles off your faces
We're still at the races
We'll be back next time
To get you...

You say we've been mashed up
You say we've been smashed up
While claiming a huge victory
Though locked inside prison
We plot our new mission
We'll be back next time
Wait and see...

Our laser exploded
Our ray gun corroded
Our planned immortality flopped
Though we're not downhearted
We haven't yet started
We'll be back next time
Just you watch...

Our caper was rumbled
Our alien stumbled
Our space rocket gave up the ghost
But we're not defeatists
Revenge will be sweetest
We'll be back next time
Then you're toast...

So don't brag you've bashed us
Don't boast that you've trashed us
Our destiny's coming real soon
For we are preparing
A crime much more daring
Next time
YOU WILL ALL MEET YOUR DOOM!...

Is it a bird? Is it a plane? No, it's...

COMIC BOOK BOY

SPECIAL SNIPPET
ALL reading is super – it will streeeeeetch your brain! If I never read superhero comic books I would not have become a poet and an author.

Comic Book Boy
(A True Story)

Superhero comics
Were all he ever read
His parents nagged away at him
To read some books instead

He searched libraries and bookshops
But nothing he could find
Could match the huge excitement
Comics caused inside his mind

He marvelled at the stories
Called characters his friends
The days dragged by
If issues had cliffhangers at the end

He loved their shiny covers
Their shape and feel and smell
Who wrote and drew and inked them too
One glance and he could tell

The villains were (usually) defeated
Though after quite a fight
The superheroes won the day
And this to him seemed right

As he became an adult
His comic reading stopped
Yet something tugged upon his heart
When passing sci-fi shops

So he bought comics once again
To get that magic back
Just like a train that was derailed
Returning to the track

He vowed he would stick with them
Beyond infinity
And write poems about superheroes and supervillains
Yes, Comic Book Boy is (still) me

THE RETURN OF THE TERRIFIC TWO!!

Superheroes Neal Zetter (Poet Perfecto) and Chris White (Illustrator Invincible) have forged an alliance once again to bring you another pulse-pounding poetry book, this time warning the Galaxy of the threat of the deadly supervillains found in these pages. Neal is an award-winning London-based comedy performance poet, author and entertainer with a huge following in schools. Since 1988 he has used his special powers to develop literacy, confidence, self-expression and creativity skills in 3-103 year olds. As well as schools he has performed in comedy clubs, theatres, pubs, music venues, the Royal Festival Hall and even at a funeral of a lost hero.

This is his fifth book with Chris White. **HERE COME THE SUPERHEROES** is featured opposite.

More on Neal: **cccpworkshops.co.uk**

Chris has used his amazing pen, pencil and computer mouse abilities to create a legion of popular characters including **Bitey the Veggie Vampire**. He has been featured on radio and TV, and travelled across Planet Earth (and light years further) to bring his cartoon and rhyme roadshows alive to humans and aliens far and wide.
This is his umpteenth book.

More on Chris: **veggievampire.com**